THE FALLING SPLENDOUR

Poems of Tennyson

The Falling Splendour

poems by Alfred Lord Tennyson
selected and introduced by
George MacBeth

illustrated by Robin Lawrie

Macmillan

Introduction © George Macbeth 1970
Illustrations © Macmillan and Co Ltd 1970

First published 1970 by
MACMILLAN AND CO LTD
London and Basingstoke
Associated companies in New York Toronto
Dublin Melbourne Johannesburg & Madras

Printed in Great Britain

CONTENTS

INTRODUCTION

Tennyson is the most famous nineteenth-century poet who is still just within the range of living memory. He was born in 1809, married in 1850, and his grandson, Sir Charles Tennyson, broadcast a personal reminiscence of him as recently as 1969. There is even an early wire recording of the poet's own voice reading his poem *The Charge of The Light Brigade* (see page 56). Despite this closeness, however, there are signs that Tennyson is only just emerging from a long period of neglect. When Edmund Blunden made a selection of his work in 1960, he called Tennyson 'the major English poet least likely to appeal to the average undergraduate'. Perhaps this is still true, but I doubt it. In an age that has accepted the eclectic romanticism of rock groups like *Tyrannosaurus Rex* and *The Incredible String Band*, the remote mystery and exoticism of Tennyson begin to seem his great merits, as the beautiful illustrations to this book very sharply bring out.

For some years after his death in 1892, Tennyson was cut down to size by younger critics. He had been too famous in his lifetime – as Byron had been before him, and Kipling was to be later – to escape censure and reaction. When Harold Nicholson published his biography of Tennyson in 1923, it was the sedate and optimistic moral judgements of the poetry that seemed to him least acceptable. He prepared an ingenious, but I think quite inaccurate, caricature of Tennyson as a writer of an excellent group of early poems who

7

was corrupted by public esteem into inflating his talent through a large range of pretentious failures, such as *The Idylls of The King*. Today, this long poem on the Arthurian legend is again visible as the masterpiece it once seemed, though perhaps looking a little less organised in structure, and a little more hectic in colouring, after its years of critical cleaning.

This sort of pictorial metaphor comes easily to mind in considering Tennyson's work. Of all the great poets of the past in English, he had the sharpest eye. (He also had the clearest ear, and I shall say more about this later.) Contemporaries often remarked on the 'pictures' in Tennyson's verses, and he strove with great care to make these vivid and coherent. *The Idylls of The King* is exactly what its title punningly says it is: a group of idols (from a Greek word meaning likeness, and later suggesting image or ghost) which will call to the eye and the mind the way the past looked. Indeed, the poem is more like a film – a moving picture – than a novel. The meaning is *in* the movement. In this selection there are three short passages and one long one from *The Idylls of The King*. On page 78, *The Birth of A New King*, and the interpretation of it by Robin Laurie, will show what I mean. Of course, there are pictures and pictures. Years of Surrealism have taught us how ingeniously Tennyson anticipated effects which even the most imaginative of Victorian artists failed to attain. The great pre-Raphaelite Burne-Jones often touched legendary and mythological themes, but he rarely gave his paintings quite the strangeness Tennyson achieved in his verse. Other contemporaries, such as Millais, interpreted particular poems, and there were many illustrated editions of Tennyson's work, including a famous one by Moxon's, his publishers, in 1857. Today, once again, we have a chance to study him in the light of an artist's imaginative response to his lines.

Of course, there is more to Tennyson than sketches for other people's paintings. I mentioned his ear. He once said that he knew the quantity of every English word except 'scissors'. He also said that when revising he always tried to 'get the geese out of the boat', by which he meant to cut down the number of irritating *s* sounds in his lines. Reading Tennyson aloud, as all poetry should be read, the extremely careful dovetailing of consonants and vowels will immediately strike you, perhaps almost as a taste of extra saliva in the mouth. This is what is often meant by the 'music' of Tennyson, as in lines like

the mellow ouzel fluted from the elm

where everything is lulling and sweet. There is also a tougher music, though, in lines like

shocks, and the splintering spear, the hard mail hewn

where we're given an almost physical feeling of the breaking and shoving of a battle. Many similar lines and phrases will leap to your ear as you read this book aloud. Occasionally, by a single word Tennyson will underline this effect, as in the grammatically incorrect but musically snug 'sung' for 'sang' in the line

the blue fly sung in the pane

in *Mariana* on page 15.

In using both his eyes and his ears, and encouraging us to do the same, Tennyson was doing no more than every poet tries to. His greatness lies in the frequency with which these senses are deployed by him to create new meaning. Auden once said that Tennyson was the 'stupidest' of the great English poets. I think he mistook skill – expressed as clarity – for lack of depth. T. S. Eliot was nearer to what Tennyson was doing when he said that in his best poems the depths and the surfaces were very near together. Tennyson thought in pictures, and he thought in sounds. If Rembrandt, or Brahms, thought profoundly, so did Tennyson. What he avoided doing was expressing thought in the language, and with the carving, of prose. In this respect, he followed in the footsteps of another great English poet to whom he seems, in his balance and his clarity, very close, Alexander Pope. In Pope, too, words are always arranged subject to the movement of the verse lines, and to the ease or difficulty with which they can be made to yield their quality when spoken aloud. In Pope, too, there is a constant concern that each phrase, each line, should be a vivid picture, even to the extent of personifying abstractions such as Prudence and Justice.

If meaning – as resonance and suggestion as well as paraphrasable content – is the root of Tennyson's purpose, the range of his subject matter is easily explained. Unlike Wordsworth, who believed

9

in directness and simplicity, after an age of over-sophistication, Tennyson believed that we must exploit every resource of fiction as well as autobiography, if a coherent and penetrating vision of the world is to be conveyed. In his dialect poems, such as *An Old Woman and her Cats*, on page 43, he can rival the humour and accuracy of the naturalistic poets, such as William Barnes of Dorset, on their own ground. Few modern playwrights could improve on this kind of faithful reflection of the way people talk. At the same time, in modern idylls, such as *The Brook*, from which the extract on page 47 is taken, Tennyson could create a sense of ordinary life in the nineteenth-century Lincolnshire of his boyhood. Parts of the English countryside are very important in Tennyson's verse, and he mirrors the landscape around his various homes at all periods of his career. Indeed, a critic in 1892 found it useful to publish a book on *The Homes and Haunts of Alfred, Lord Tennyson*, where he relates the poet's descriptive passages to the houses he lived in at Somersby in Lincolnshire, Farringford on the Isle of Wight, and Aldworth in Sussex. (One less important home that he illustrates with a fine line engraving is the house in Montpelier Row, Twickenham, near where I live, where a blue plaque commemorates Tennyson's period of residence in the early 1850s.

Despite his concern with his natural surroundings, however, it remains in wilder flights of fantasy, as when handling the Arthurian legends, that Tennyson seems able to release the densest range of meaning and association. What he says about human relations in *The Decline of The Kingdom* is sublime and terrible, but it also has a down-to-earth ring of truth. There will always be jealousy, betrayal and remorse, and Tennyson gives these huge emotions a ritual ghostliness and warning clangour in treating them through the symbols of a strange far-off world of knights and ladies. The distance adds precision as well as enchantment to the view. We see the wood as well as the trees, as we do in Shakespeare's *Histories*. Perhaps Shakespeare is a good name to end with. He is the only English poet whose range, depth and skill are greater than Tennyson's.

GEORGE MACBETH

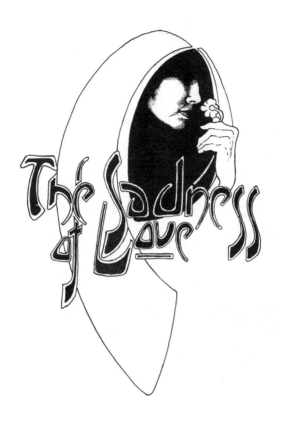

MARIANA

Mariana in the moated grange
(Measure for Measure)

WITH blackest moss the flower-plots
  Were thickly crusted, one and all:
The rusted nails fell from the knots
  That held the pear to the gable-wall.
The broken sheds looked sad and strange :
  Unlifted was the clinking latch;
  Weeded and worn the ancient thatch
Upon the lonely moated grange.
    She only said, 'My life is dreary,
      He cometh not,' she said;
    She said, 'I am aweary, aweary,
      I would that I were dead!'

Her tears fell with the dews at even;
　　Her tears fell ere the dews were dried;
She could not look on the sweet heaven,
　　Either at morn or eventide.
After the flitting of the bats,
　　When thickest dark did trance the sky,
　　She drew her casement-curtain by,
And glanced athwart the glooming flats.
　　　　She only said, 'The night is dreary,
　　　　　　He cometh not,' she said;
　　　　She said, 'I am aweary, aweary,
　　　　　　I would that I were dead!'

Upon the middle of the night,
　　Waking she heard the night-fowl crow:
The cock sung out an hour ere light:
　　From the dark fen the oxen's low
Came to her: without hope of change,
　　In sleep she seemed to walk forlorn,
　　Till cold winds woke the gray-eyed morn.
About the lonely moated grange.
　　　　She only said, 'The day is dreary,
　　　　　　He cometh not,' she said;
　　　　She said, 'I am aweary, aweary,
　　　　　　I would that I were dead!'

About a stone-cast from the wall
　　A sluice with blackened waters slept,
And o'er it many, round and small,
　　The clustered marish-mosses crept.
Hard by a poplar shook alway,
　　All silver-green with gnarlèd bark:
　　For leagues no other tree did mark
The level waste, the rounding gray.
　　　　She only said, 'My life is dreary,
　　　　　　He cometh not,' she said;
　　　　She said, 'I am aweary, aweary,
　　　　　　I would that I were dead!'

And ever when the moon was low,
  And the shrill winds were up and away,
In the white curtain, to and fro,
  She saw the gusty shadow sway.
But when the moon was very low,
  And wild winds bound within their cell,
  The shadow of the poplar fell
Upon her bed, across her brow.
    She only said, 'The night is dreary,
      He cometh not,' she said;
    She said, 'I am aweary, aweary,
      I would that I were dead!'

All day within the dreamy house,
  The doors upon their hinges creaked;
The blue fly sung in the pane; the mouse
  Behind the mouldering wainscot shrieked,
Or from the crevice peered about.
  Old faces glimmered through the doors,
  Old footsteps trod the upper floors,
Old voices called her from without.
    She only said, 'My life is dreary,
      He cometh not,' she said;
    She said, 'I am aweary, aweary,
      I would that I were dead!'

The sparrow's chirrup on the roof,
  The slow clock ticking, and the sound
Which to the wooing wind aloof
  The poplar made, did all confound
Her sense; but most she loathed the hour
  When the thick-moted sunbeam lay
  Athwart the chambers, and the day
Was sloping toward his western bower.
    Then, said she, 'I am very dreary,
      He will not come,' she said;
    She wept, 'I am aweary, aweary,
      Oh God, that I were dead!'

'COME NOT, WHEN I AM DEAD'

COME not, when I am dead,
　　To drop thy foolish tears upon my grave,
To trample round my fallen head,
　　And vex the unhappy dust thou wouldst not save.
There let the wind sweep and the plover cry;
　　　　But thou, go by.

Child, if it were thine error or thy crime
　　I care no longer, being all unblest:
Wed whom thou wilt, but I am sick of Time,
　　And I desire to rest.
Pass on, weak heart, and leave me where I lie:
　　　　Go by, go by.

A DIRGE

Now is done thy long day's work;
Fold thy palms across thy breast,
Fold thine arms, turn to thy rest.
    Let them rave.
Shadows of the silver birk
Sweep the green that folds thy grave.
    Let them rave.

II

Thee nor carketh care nor slander;
Nothing but the small cold worm
Fretteth thine enshrouded form.
    Let them rave.
Light and shadow ever wander
O'er the green that folds thy grave.
    Let them rave.

III

Thou wilt not turn upon thy bed;
Chaunteth not the brooding bee
Sweeter tones than calumny?
    Let them rave.
Thou wilt never raise thine head
From the green that folds thy grave.
    Let them rave.

IV

Crocodiles wept tears for thee;
The woodbine and eglatere
Drip sweeter dews than traitor's tear.
    Let them rave.
Rain makes music in the tree
O'er the green that folds thy grave.
    Let them rave.

V

Round thee blow, self-pleachèd deep,
Bramble roses, faint and pale,
And long purples of the dale.
    Let them rave.
These in every shower creep
Through the green that folds thy grave.
    Let them rave.

VI

The gold-eyed kingcups fine;
The frail bluebell peereth over
Rare broidry of the purple clover,
    Let them rave.
Kings have no such couch as thine,
As the green that folds thy grave.
    Let them rave.

VII

Wild words wander here and there:
God's great gift of speech abused
Makes thy memory confused:
    But let them rave.
The balm-cricket carols clear
In the green that folds thy grave.
    Let them rave.

THE LADY OF SHALOTT

PART I

On either side the river lie
Long fields of barley and of rye,
That clothe the wold and meet the sky;
And through the field the road runs by
    To many-towered Camelot;
And up and down the people go,
Gazing where the lilies blow
Round an island there below,
    The island of Shalott.

Willows whiten, aspens quiver,
Little breezes dusk and shiver
Through the wave that runs for ever
By the island in the river
    Flowing down to Camelot.
Four gray walls, and four gray towers,
Overlook a space of flowers,
And the silent isle imbowers
    The Lady of Shalott.

By the margin, willow-veiled,
Slide the heavy barges trailed
By slow horses; and unhailed
The shallop flitteth silken-sailed
    Skimming down to Camelot:
But who hath seen her wave her hand?
Or at the casement seen her stand?
Or is she known in all the land,
    The Lady of Shalott?

Only reapers, reaping early
In among the bearded barley
Hear a song that echoes cheerly
From the river winding clearly,
    Down to towered Camelot:
And by the moon the reaper weary,
Piling sheaves in uplands airy,
Listening, whispers ' 'Tis the fairy
    Lady of Shalott.'

PART II

There she weaves by night and day
A magic web with colours gay.
She has heard a whisper say,
A curse is on her if she stay
        To look down to Camelot.
She knows not what the curse may be,
And so she weaveth steadily,
And little other care hath she,
        The Lady of Shalott.

And moving through a mirror clear
That hangs before her all the year,
Shadows of the world appear.
There she sees the highway near
        Winding down to Camelot:
There the river eddy whirls,
And there the surly village/churls,
And the red cloaks of market girls,
        Pass onward from Shalott.

Sometimes a troop of damsels glad,
An abbot on an ambling pad,
Sometimes a curly shepherd/lad,
Or long/haired page in crimson clad,
        Goes by to towered Camelot;
And sometimes through the mirror blue
The knights come riding two and two:
She hath no loyal knight and true,
        The Lady of Shalott.

But in her web she still delights
To weave the mirror's magic sights,
For often through the silent nights
A funeral, with plumes and lights
    And music, went to Camelot:
Or when the moon was overhead,
Came two young lovers lately wed;
'I am half sick of shadows,' said
    The Lady of Shalott.

PART III

A bow-shot from her bower-eaves,
He rode between the barley-sheaves,
The sun came dazzling through the leaves,
And flamed upon the brazen greaves
    Of bold Sir Lancelot.
A red-cross knight for ever kneeled
To a lady in his shield,
That sparkled on the yellow field,
    Beside remote Shalott.

The gemmy bridle glittered free,
Like to some branch of stars we see
Hung in the golden Galaxy.
The bridle bells rang merrily
    As he rode down to Camelot:
And from his blazoned baldric slung
A mighty silver bugle hung,
And as he rode his armour rung,
    Beside remote Shalott.

All in the blue unclouded weather
Thick-jewelled shone the saddle-leather,
The helmet and the helmet-feather
Burned like one burning flame together,
    As he rode down to Camelot.
As often through the purple night,
Below the starry clusters bright,
Some bearded meteor, trailing light,
    Moves over still Shalott.

His broad clear brow in sunlight glowed;
On burnished hooves his war-horse trode;
From underneath his helmet flowed
His coal-black curls as on he rode,
    As he rode down to Camelot.
From the bank and from the river
He flashed into the crystal mirror,
'Tirra lirra,' by the river
    Sang Sir Lancelot.

She left the web, she left the loom,
She made three paces through the room,
She saw the water-lily bloom,
She saw the helmet and the plume,
    She looked down to Camelot.
Out flew the web and floated wide;
The mirror cracked from side to side;
'The curse is come upon me,' cried
    The Lady of Shalott.

PART IV

In the stormy east-wind straining,
The pale yellow woods were waning,
The broad stream in his banks complaining.
Heavily the low sky raining
    Over towered Camelot;
Down she came and found a boat
Beneath a willow left afloat,
And round about the prow she wrote
    The Lady of Shalott.

And down the river's dim expanse
Like some bold seër in a trance,
Seeing all his own mischance –
With a glassy countenance
    Did she look to Camelot.
And at the closing of the day
She loosed the chain, and down she lay;
The broad stream bore her far away,
    The Lady of Shalott.

Lying, robed in snowy white
That loosely flew to left and right –
The leaves upon her falling light –
Through the noises of the night
    She floated down to Camelot:
And as the boat-head wound along
The willowy hills and fields among,
They heard her singing her last song,
    The Lady of Shalott.

Heard a carol, mournful, holy,
Chanted loudly, chanted lowly,
Till her blood was frozen slowly,
And her eyes were darkened wholly,
 Turned to towered Camelot.
For ere she reached upon the tide
The first house by the water-side,
Singing in her song she died,
 The Lady of Shalott.

Under tower and balcony,
By garden-wall and gallery,
A gleaming shape she floated by,
Dead-pale between the houses high,
 Silent into Camelot.
Out upon the wharfs they came,
Knight and burgher, lord and dame,
And round the prow they read her name,
 The Lady of Shalott.

Who is this? and what is here?
And in the lighted palace near
Died the sound of royal cheer;
And they crossed themselves for fear,
 All the knights at Camelot:
But Lancelot mused a little space;
He said, 'She has a lovely face;
God in his mercy lend her grace,
 The Lady of Shalott.'

'NOW SLEEPS THE CRIMSON PETAL'

'Now sleeps the crimson petal, now the white;
Nor waves the cypress in the palace walk;
Nor winks the gold fin in the porphyry font:
The fire-fly wakens: waken thou with me.

'Now droops the milkwhite peacock like a ghost,
And like a ghost she glimmers on to me.

'Now lies the Earth all Danaë to the stars,
And all thy heart lies open unto me.

'Now slides the silent meteor on, and leaves
A shining furrow, as thy thoughts in me.

'Now folds the lily all her sweetness up,
And slips into the bosom of the lake:
So fold thyself, my dearest, thou, and slip
Into my bosom and be lost in me.'

(FROM: *The Princess*)

'COME INTO THE GARDEN, MAUD'

I

Come into the garden, Maud,
  For the black bat, night, has flown,
Come into the garden, Maud,
  I am here at the gate alone;
And the woodbine spices are wafted abroad,
  And the musk of the rose is blown.

II

For a breeze of morning moves,
  And the planet of Love is on high,
Beginning to faint in the light that she loves
  On a bed of daffodil sky,
To faint in the light of the sun she loves,
  To faint in his light, and to die.

III

All night have the roses heard
  The flute, violin, bassoon;
All night has the casement jessamine stirred
  To the dancers dancing in tune;
Till a silence fell with the waking bird,
  And a hush with the setting moon.

IV

I said to the lily, 'There is but one
  With whom she has heart to be gay.
When will the dancers leave her alone?
  She is weary of dance and play.'
Now half to the setting moon are gone,
  And half to the rising day;
Low on the sand and loud on the stone
  The last wheel echoes away.

V

I said to the rose, 'The brief night goes
  In babble and revel and wine.
O young lord‑lover, what sighs are those,
  For one that will never be thine?
But mine, but mine,' so I sware to the rose,
  'For ever and ever, mine.'

VI

And the soul of the rose went into my blood,
  As the music clashed in the hall;
And long by the garden lake I stood,
  For I heard your rivulet fall
From the lake to the meadow and on to the wood,
  Our wood, that is dearer than all;

VII

From the meadow your walks have left so sweet
  That whenever a March‑wind sighs
He sets the jewel‑print of your feet
  In violets blue as your eyes,
To the woody hollows in which we meet
  And the valleys of Paradise.

VIII

The slender acacia would not shake
  One long milk‑bloom on the tree;
The white lake‑blossom fell into the lake
  As the pimpernel dozed on the lea;
But the rose was awake all night for your sake,
  Knowing your promise to me;
The lilies and roses were all awake,
  They sighed for the dawn and thee.

IX

Queen rose of the rosebud garden of girls,
  Come hither, the dances are done,
In gloss of satin and glimmer of pearls,
  Queen lily and rose in one;
Shine out, little head, sunning over with curls,
  To the flowers, and be their sun.

X

There has fallen a splendid tear
  From the passion-flower at the gate.
She is coming, my dove, my dear;
  She is coming, my life, my fate;
The red rose cries, 'She is near, she is near;'
  And the white rose weeps, 'She is late;'
The larkspur listens, 'I hear, I hear;'
  And the lily whispers, 'I wait.'

XI

She is coming, my own, my sweet;
  Were it ever so airy a tread,
My heart would hear her and beat,
  Were it earth in an earthy bed;
My dust would hear her and beat,
  Had I lain for a century dead;
Would start and tremble under her feet,
  And blossom in purple and red.

(FROM: Maud)

'BIRDS IN THE HIGH HALL-GARDEN'

I

Birds in the high Hall-garden
  When twilight was falling,
Maud, Maud, Maud, Maud,
  They were crying and calling.

II

Where was Maud? in our wood;
    And I, who else, was with her,
Gathering woodland lilies,
    Myriads blow together.

III

Birds in our wood sang
    Ringing through the valleys,
Maud is here, here, here
    In among the lilies.

IV

I kissed her slender hand,
    She took the kiss sedately;
Maud is not seventeen,
    But she is tall and stately.

V

I to cry out on pride
    Who have won her favour!
O Maud were sure of Heaven
    If lowliness could save her.

VI

I know the way she went
    Home with her maiden posy,
For her feet have touched the meadows
    And left the daisies rosy.

VII

Birds in the high Hall-garden
    Were crying and calling to her,
Where is Maud, Maud, Maud?
    One is come to woo her.

VIII

Look, a horse at the door,
    And little King Charley snarling,
Go back, my lord, across the moor,
    You are not her darling.

(FROM: *Maud*)

THE EAGLE
Fragment

HE clasps the crag with crookèd hands;
Close to the sun in lonely lands,
Ringed with the azure world, he stands.

The wrinkled sea beneath him crawls;
He watches from his mountain walls,
And like a thunderbolt he falls.

THE BLACKBIRD

O BLACKBIRD! sing me something well:
   While all the neighbours shoot thee round,
   I keep smooth plats of fruitful ground,
Where thou mayst warble, eat and dwell.

The espaliers and the standards all
   Are thine; the range of lawn and park:
   The unnetted black-hearts ripen dark,
All thine, against the garden wall.

Yet, though I spared thee all the spring,
   Thy sole delight is, sitting still,
   With that gold dagger of thy bill
To fret the summer jenneting.

A golden bill! the silver tongue,
   Cold February loved, is dry:
   Plenty corrupts the melody
That made thee famous once, when young:

And in the sultry garden-squares,
   Now thy flute-notes are changed to coarse,
   I hear thee not at all, or hoarse
As when a hawker hawks his wares.

Take warning! he that will not sing
   While yon sun prospers in the blue,
   Shall sing for want, ere leaves are new,
Caught in the frozen palms of Spring.

SONG – THE OWL

I

WHEN cats run home and light is come,
  And dew is cold upon the ground,
And the far-off stream is dumb,
  And the whirring sail goes round,
  And the whirring sail goes round;
    Alone and warming his five wits,
    The white owl in the belfry sits.

II

When merry milkmaids click the latch,
  And rarely smells the new-mown hay,
And the cock hath sung beneath the thatch
  Twice or thrice his roundelay,
  Twice or thrice his roundelay;
  Alone and warming his five wits,
    The white owl in the belfry sits.

THE GOOSE

I KNEW an old wife lean and poor,
   Her rags scarce held together;
There strode a stranger to the door,
   And it was windy weather.

He held a goose upon his arm,
   He uttered rhyme and reason,
'Here, take the goose, and keep you warm,
   It is a stormy season.'

She caught the white goose by the leg,
   A goose – 'twas no great matter.
The goose let fall a golden egg
   With cackle and with clatter.

She dropt the goose, and caught the pelf,
   And ran to tell her neighbours;
And blessed herself, and cursed herself,
   And rested from her labours.

And feeding high, and living soft,
   Grew plump and able-bodied;
Until the grave churchwarden doffed,
   The parson smirked and nodded.

So sitting, served by man and maid,
   She felt her heart grow prouder:
But ah! the more the white goose laid
   It clacked and cackled louder.

It cluttered here, it chuckled there;
   It stirred the old wife's mettle:
She shifted in her elbow-chair,
   And hurled the pan and kettle.

'A quinsy choke thy cursèd note!'
    Then waxed her anger stronger.
'Go, take the goose, and wring her throat,
    I will not bear it longer.'

Then yelped the cur, and yawled the cat;
    Ran Gaffer, stumbled Gammer.
The goose flew this way and flew that,
    And filled the house with clamour.

As head and heels upon the floor
    They floundered all together,
There strode a stranger to the door,
    And it was windy weather:

He took the goose upon his arm,
    He uttered words of scorning;
'So keep you cold, or keep you warm,
    It is a stormy morning.'

The wild wind rang from park and plain,
    And round the attics rumbled,
Till all the tables danced again,
    And half the chimneys tumbled.

The glass blew in, the fire blew out,
    The blast was hard and harder.
Her cap blew off, her gown blew up,
    And a whirlwind cleared the larder:

And while on all sides breaking loose
    Her household fled the danger,
Quoth she, 'The Devil take the goose,
    And God forget the stranger!'

A POET'S TREE

Look what love the puddle-pated squarecaps have for me!
I am Milton's mulberry, Milton's Milton's mulberry –
But they whipt and rusticated him that planted me,
Milton's Milton's mulberry, Milton's Milton's mulberry.
Old and hollow, somewhat crookèd in the shoulders as you
      see,
Full of summer foliage yet but propt and padded curiously,
I would sooner have been planted by the hand that planted
      me,
Than have grown in Paradise and dropped my fruit on
      Adam's knee –
Look what love the tiny-witted trenchers have for me.

                  (*Milton's Mulberry*)

SPLEEN AT A COUNTRY INN

Black Bull of Aldgate, may thy horns rot from the sockets!
For, jingling threepence, porter's pay, in hungry pockets,
And thirty times at least beneath thy doorway stepping
I've waited for this lousy coach that runs to Epping.
Ill luck befall thee, that hast made me so splenetic,
Through all thy holes and closets up from tap to attic,
Through all thy boys and bootses, chambermaids, and waiters,
And yonder booking-office-clerk in fustian gaiters.
Black Bull of Aldgate! mayst thou more miscarry
Than ever hasty Clement's did with bloated Harry!

                  (*'Black Bull of Aldgate'*)

MARRIAGE HINDERED BY MONEY

I

Dosn't thou 'ear my 'erse's legs, as they canters awaäy?
Proputty, proputty, proputty – that's what I 'ears 'em saäy.
Proputty, proputty, proputty – Sam, thou's an ass for thy .
    paaïns:
Theer's moor sense i' one o' 'is legs nor in all thy braaïns.

II

Woä – theer's a craw to pluck wi' tha, Sam: yon's parson's
    'ouse –
Dosn't thou knaw that a man mun be eäther a man or a
    mouse?
Time to think on it then; for thou'll be twenty to weeäk.
Proputty, proputty – woä then woä – let ma 'ear mysén speäk.

III

Me an' thy muther, Sammy, 'as beän a-talkin' o' thee;
Thou's beän talkin' to muther, an' she beän a tellin' it me.
Thou'll not marry for munny – thou's sweet upo' parson's lass –
Noä – thou'll marry for luvv – an' we boäth on us thinks tha
    an ass.

IV

Seeä'd her todaäy goä by – Saäint's-daäy – they was ringing the
    bells.
She's a beauty thou thinks – an' soä is scoors o' gells,
Them as 'as munny an' all – wot's a beauty? – the flower as
    blaws.
But proputty, proputty sticks, an' proputty, proputty graws.

V

Do'ant be stunt: taäke time: I knaws what maäkes tha sa
    mad.
Warn't I craäzed fur the lasses mysén when I wur a lad?
But I knawed a Quaäker feller as often 'as towd ma this:
'Doänt thou marry for munny, but goä wheer munny is!'

VI

An' I went wheer munny war: an' thy muther coom to 'and,
Wi' lots o' munny laaïd by, an' a nicetish bit o' land.
Maäybe she warn't a beauty: – I niver giv it a thowt –
But warn't she as good to cuddle an' kiss as a lass as 'ant
    nowt?

VII

Parson's lass 'ant nowt, an' she weänt 'a nowt when 'e's deäd,
Mun be a guvness, lad, or summut, and addle her breäd:
Why? fur 'e's nobbut a curate, an' weänt niver git hissen
    clear,
An' 'e maäde the bed as 'e ligs on afoor 'e coomed to the
    shere.

An' thin 'e coomed to the parish wi' lots o' Varsity debt,
Stook to his taaïl they did, an' 'e 'ant got shut on 'em yet.
An' 'e ligs on 'is back i' the grip, wi' noän to lend 'im a
    shuvv,
Woorse nor a far⸲weltered yowe: fur, Sammy, 'e married fur
    luvv.

IX

Luvv? what's luvv? thou can luvv thy lass an' 'er munny too,
Maakin' 'em goä togither as they've good right to do.
Could'n I luvv thy muther by cause o' 'er munny laaïd by?
Naäy – fur I luvved 'er a vast sight moor fur it: reäson why.

X

Ay an' thy muther says thou wants to marry the lass,
Cooms of a gentleman burn: an' we boäth on us think tha
    an ass.
Woä then, proputty, wiltha? – an ass as near as mays nowt –
Woä then, wiltha? dangtha! – the bees is as fell as owt.

XI

Breäk me a bit o' the esh for his 'eäd lad, out o' the fence!
Gentleman burn! what's gentleman burn? is it shillins an'
    pence?
Proputty, proputty's ivrything 'ere, an', Sammy, I'm blest
If it isn't the saäme oop yonder, fur them as 'as it's the best.

XII

Tis'n them as 'as munny as breäks into 'ouses an' steäls,
Them as 'as coäts to their backs an' taäkes their regular
    meäls.
Noä, but it's them as niver knaws wheer a meäl's to be 'ad.
Taäke my word for it, Sammy, the poor in a loomp is bad.

Them or thir feythers, tha sees, mun 'a beän a laäzy lot,
Fur work mun 'a gone to the gittin' whiniver munny was got.
Feyther 'ad ammost nowt; leästways 'is munny was 'id.
But 'e tued an' moiled 'issén deäd, an 'e died a good un, 'e
did.

XIV

Look thou theer wheer Wrigglesby beck cooms out by the
'ill!
Feyther run oop to the farm, an' I runs oop to the mill;
An' I'll run oop to the brig, an' that thou'll live to see;
And if thou marries a good un I'll leäve the land to thee.

XV

Thim's my noätions, Sammy, wheerby I means to stick;
But if thou marries a bad un, I'll leäve the land to Dick. –
Coom oop, proputty, proputty – that's what I 'ears 'im saäy –
Proputty, proputty, proputty – canter an' canter awaäy.

(*Northern Farmer: New Style*)

AN OLD WOMAN AND HER CATS

I

ROBBY, git down wi'tha, wilt tha? let Steevie coom oop o'
    my knee.
Steevie, my lad, thou 'ed very nigh been the Steevie fur me!
Robby wur fust to be sewer, 'e wur burn an' bred i' the 'ouse,
But thou be es 'ansom a tabby es iver patted a mouse.

II

An' I beänt not vaäin, but I knaws I 'ed led tha a quieter life
Nor her wi' the hepitaph yonder! 'A faäithful an' loovin' wife!
An' 'cos o' thy farm by the beck, an' thy windmill oop o'
    the croft,
Tha thowt tha would marry ma, did tha? but that wur a bit
    ower soft,

Thaw thou was es soäber es daäy, wi' a niced red faäce, an'
  es cleän
Es a shillin' fresh fro' the mint wi' a bran-new 'eäd o' the
  Queeän,
An' thy farmin' es cleän es thysen, fur, Steevie, tha kep' it sa
  neät
That I niver not spied sa much es a poppy along wi' the
  wheät,
An' the wool of a thistle a-flyin' an' seeädin' tha haäted to see;
'Twur es bad es a battle-twig¹ 'ere i' my oän blue chaumber
  to me.
Ay, roob thy whiskers ageän ma, fur I could 'a taäen to tha
  well,
But fur thy bairns, poor Steevie, a bouncin' boy an' a gell.

III

An' thou was es fond o' thy bairns es I be mysen o' my cats,
But I niver not wished fur childer, I hevn't naw likin' fur
  brats;
Pretty anew when ya dresses 'em oop, an' they goäs fur a
  walk,
Or sits wi' their 'ands afoor 'em, an' doesn't not 'inder the
  talk!
But their bottles o' pap, an' their mucky bibs, an' the clats
  an' the clouts,
An' their mashin' their toys to pieäces an' maäkin' ma deäf
  wi' their shouts,
An' hallus a-joompin' about ma as if they was set upo'
  springs,
An' a haxin' ma hawkard questions, an' saäyin' ondecent
  things,
An' a-callin' ma 'hugly' mayhap to my faäce, or a teärin'
  my gown –
Dear! dear! dear! I mun part them Tommies – Steevie git
  down.

Ye be wuss nor the men*tommies, you. I telled ya, na moor
    o' that!
Tom, lig theere o' the cushion, an' tother Tom 'ere o' the
    mat.

V

Theere! I ha' mastered *them*! Hed I married the Tommies –
    O Lord,
To loove an' obaäy the Tommies! I couldn't 'a stuck by my
    word.
To be hordered about, an' waäked, when Molly 'd put out
    the light,
By a man coomin' in wi' a hiccup at ony hour o' the night!
An' the taäble staäined wi' 'is aäle, an' the mud o' 'is boots o'
    the stairs,
An' the stink o' 'is pipe i' the 'ouse, an' the mark o 'is 'eäd
    o' the chairs!
An' noän o' my four sweet*arts 'ud 'a let me 'a hed my oän
    waäy,
Sa I likes 'em best wi' taäils when they 'evn't a word to saäy.
(FROM: The Spinster's Sweet*Arts)

    [1] *battle-twig*: 'earwig'

A KISS WHILE MILKING

Shame upon you, Robin,
  Shame upon you now!
Kiss me would you? with my hands
  Milking the cow?
  Daisies grow again,
  Kingcups blow again,
And you came and kissed me milking the cow.

Robin came behind me,
  Kissed me well I vow;
Cuff him could I? with my hands
  Milking the cow?
  Swallows fly again,
  Cuckoos cry again,
And you came and kissed me milking the cow.

Come, Robin, Robin,
     Come and kiss me now;
Help it can I? with my hands
     Milking the cow?
     Ringdoves coo again,
     All things woo again.
Come behind and kiss me milking the cow!

(FROM: *Queen Mary*)

BOREDOM IN A GOOD CAUSE

'SHE told me. She and James had quarrelled. Why?
What cause of quarrel? None, she said, no cause;
James had no cause: but when I prest the cause,
I learnt that James had flickering jealousies
Which angered her. Who angered James? I said.
But Katie snatched her eyes at once from mine,
And sketching with her slender pointed foot
Some figure like a wizard pentagram
On garden gravel, let my query pass
Unclaimed, in flushing silence, till I asked
If James were coming. "Coming every day,"
She answered, "ever longing to explain,
But evermore her father came across
With some long-winded tale, and broke him short;
And James departed vext with him and her."
How could I help her? "Would I – was it wrong?"
(Claspt hands and that petitionary grace
Of sweet seventeen subdued me ere she spoke)
"O would I take her father for one hour,
For one half-hour, and let him talk to me!"
And even while she spoke, I saw where James
Made toward us, like a wader in the surf,
Beyond the brook, waist-deep in meadow-sweet.

'O Katie, what I suffered for your sake!
For in I went, and called old Philip out
To show the farm: full willingly he rose:

He led me through the short sweet-smelling lanes
Of his wheat-suburb, babbling as he went.
He praised his land, his horses, his machines;
He praised his ploughs, his cows, his hogs, his dogs;
He praised his hens, his geese, his guinea-hens;
His pigeons, who in session on their roofs
Approved him, bowing at their own deserts:
Then from the plaintive mother's teat he took
Her blind and shuddering puppies, naming each,
And naming those, his friends, for whom they were:
Then crost the common into Darnley chase
To show Sir Arthur's deer. In copse and fern
Twinkled the innumerable ear and tail.
Then, seated on a serpent-rooted beech,
He pointed out a pasturing colt, and said:
"That was the four-year-old I sold the Squire.'
And there he told a long long-winded tale
Of how the Squire had seen the colt at grass,
And how it was the thing his daughter wished,
And how he sent the bailiff to the farm
To learn the price, and what the price he asked,
And how the bailiff swore that he was mad,
But he stood firm; and so the matter hung;
He gave them line: and five days after that
He met the bailiff at the Golden Fleece,
Who then and there had offered something more,
But he stood firm; and so the matter hung;
He knew the man; the colt would fetch its price;
He gave them line: and how by chance at last
(It might be May or April, he forgot,
The last of April or the first of May)
He found the bailiff riding by the farm,
And, talking from the point, he drew him in,
And there he mellowed all his heart with ale,
Until they closed a bargain, hand in hand.

'Then, while I breathed in sight of haven, he,
Poor fellow, could he help it? recommenced,

And ran through all the coltish chronicle,
Wild Will, Black Bess, Tantivy, Tallyho,
Reform, White Rose, Bellerophon, the Jilt
Arbaces, and Phenomenon, and the rest,
Till, not to die a listener, I arose,
And with me Philip, talking still; and so
We turned our foreheads from the falling sun,
And following our own shadows thrice as long
As when they followed us from Philip's door,
Arrived, and found the sun of sweet content
Re-risen in Katie's eyes, and all things well.

(FROM: The Brook)

AUDLEY COURT

'THE Bull, the Fleece are crammed, and not a room
For love or money. Let us picnic there
At Audley Court.'
                I spoke, while Audley feast
Hummed like a hive all round the narrow quay,
To Francis, with a basket on his arm,
To Francis just alighted from the boat,
And breathing of the sea. 'With all my heart,'
Said Francis. Then we shouldered through the swarm,
And rounded by the stillness of the beach
To where the bay runs up its latest horn.

We left the dying ebb that faintly lipped
That flat red granite; so by many a sweep
Of meadow smooth from aftermath we reached
The griffin-guarded gates, and passed through all
The pillared dusk of sounding sycamores,
And crossed the garden to the gardener's lodge,
With all its casements bedded, and its walls
And chimneys muffled in the leafy vine.

There, on a slope of orchard, Francis laid
A damask napkin wrought with horse and hound,
Brought out a dusky loaf that smelt of home,
And, half-cut-down, a pasty costly-made,
Where quail and pigeon, lark and leveret lay,
Like fossils of the rock, with golden yolks
Imbedded and injellied; last, with these,
A flask of cider from his father's vats,
Prime, which I knew; and so we sat and eat
And talked old matters over; who was dead
Who married, who was like to be, and how
The races went, and who would rent the hall:
Then touched upon the game, how scarce it was
This season; glancing thence, discussed the farm,
The four-field system, and the price of grain;
And struck upon the corn-laws, where we split,
And came again together on the king
With heated faces; till he laughed aloud;
And, while the blackbird on the pippin hung
To hear him, clapt his hand in mine and sang –

  'Oh! who would fight and march and countermarch,
Be shot for sixpence in a battle-field,
And shovelled up into some bloody trench
Where no one knows? but let me live my life.
  'Oh! who would cast and balance at a desk,
Perched like a crow upon a three-legged stool,
Till all his juice is dried, and all his joints
Are full of chalk? but let me live my life.

  'Who'd serve the state? for if I carved my name
Upon the cliffs that guard my native land,
I might as well have traced it in the sands;
The sea wastes all: but let me live my life.
  'Oh! who would love? I wooed a woman once
But she was sharper than an eastern wind,
And all my heart turned from her, as a thorn
Turns from the sea; but let me live my life.'

He sang his song, and I replied with mine:
I found it in a volume, all of songs,
Knocked down to me, when old Sir Robert's pride,
His books – the more the pity, so I said –
Came to the hammer here in March – and this –
I set the words, and added names I knew.

'Sleep, Ellen Aubrey, sleep, and dream of me:
Sleep, Ellen, folded in thy sister's arm,
And sleeping, haply dream her arm is mine.
'Sleep, Ellen, folded in Emilia's arm;
Emilia, fairer than all else but thou,
For thou art fairer than all else that is.
'Sleep, breathing health and peace upon her breast:
Sleep, breathing love and trust against her lip:
I go tonight: I come tomorrow morn.
'I go, but I return: I would I were
The pilot of the darkness and the dream.
Sleep, Ellen Aubrey, love, and dream of me.'

So sang we each to either, Francis Hale,
The farmer's son, who lived across the bay,
My friend; and I, that having wherewithal,
And in the fallow leisure of my life
A rolling stone of here and everywhere,
Did what I would; but ere the night we rose
And sauntered home beneath a moon, that, just
In crescent, dimly rained about the leaf
Twilights of airy silver, till we reached
The limit of the hills; and as we sank
From rock to rock upon the glooming quay,
The town was hushed beneath us: lower down
The bay was oily calm; the harbour-buoy,
Sole star of phosphorescence in the calm,
With one green sparkle ever and anon
Dipt by itself, and we were glad at heart.

THREE DEAD FRIENDS

Nightingales warbled without,
  Within was weeping for thee:
Shadows of three dead men
  Walked in the walks with me,
  Shadows of three dead men and thou wast one
      of the three.

Nightingales sang in his woods:
  The Master was far away:
Nightingales warbled and sang
  Of a passion that lasts but a day;
  Still in the house in his coffin the Prince of
      courtesy lay.

Two dead men have I known
  In courtesy like to thee:
Two dead men have I loved
  With a love that ever will be:
  Three dead men have I loved and thou art last
      of the three.

SONNET
FOR POLAND
Written on hearing of the
outbreak of the Polish Insurrection

Blow ye the trumpet, gather from afar
The hosts to battle: be not bought and sold.
Arise, brave Poles, the boldest of the bold;
Break through your iron shackles – fling them far.
O for those days of Piast, ere the Czar
Grew to this strength among his deserts cold;
When even to Moscow's cupolas were rolled
The growing murmurs of the Polish war!
Now must your noble anger blaze out more
Than when from Sobieski, clan by clan,
The Moslem myriads fell, and fled before –
Than when Zamoysky smote the Tatar Khan;
Than earlier, when on the Baltic shore
Boleslas drove the Pomeranian.   *(Sonnet)*

THE CHARGE OF THE LIGHT BRIGADE

I

Half a league, half a league,
  Half a league onward,
All in the valley of Death
  Rode the six hundred.
'Forward, the Light Brigade!
Charge for the guns!' he said:
Into the valley of Death
  Rode the six hundred.

II

'Forward, the Light Brigade!'
Was there a man dismayed?
Not though the soldier knew
  Some one had blundered:
Their's not to make reply,
Their's not to reason why,
Their's but to do and die:
Into the valley of Death
  Rode the six hundred.

III

Cannon to right of them,
Cannon to left of them,
Cannon in front of them
  Volleyed and thundered;
Stormed at with shot and shell,
Boldly they rode and well,
Into the jaws of Death,
Into the mouth of Hell
  Rode the six hundred.

IV

Flashed all their sabres bare,
Flashed as they turned in air
Sabring the gunners there,
Charging an army, while
  All the world wondered:
Plunged in the battery-smoke
Right through the line they broke;
Cossack and Russian
Reeled from the sabre-stroke
  Shattered and sundered.
Then they rode back, but not
  Not the six hundred.

V

Cannon to right of them,
Cannon to left of them,
Cannon behind them
   Volleyed and thundered;
Stormed at with shot and shell,
While horse and hero fell,
They that had fought so well
Came through the jaws of Death,
Back from the mouth of Hell,
All that was left of them,
   Left of six hundred.

VI

When can their glory fade?
O the wild charge they made!
   All the world wondered.
Honour the charge they made!
Honour the Light Brigade,
   Noble six hundred!

THE REVENGE
A Ballad of the Fleet

I

At Flores in the Azores Sir Richard Grenville lay,
And a pinnace, like a fluttered bird, came flying from far away:
'Spanish ships of war at sea! we have sighted fifty-three!'
Then sware Lord Thomas Howard: ' 'Fore God I am no
    coward;
But I cannot meet them here, for my ships are out of gear,
And the half my men are sick. I must fly, but follow quick.
We are six ships of the line; can we fight with fifty-three?'

II

Then spake Sir Richard Grenville: 'I know you are no coward;
You fly them for a moment to fight with them again.
But I've ninety men and more that are lying sick ashore.
I should count myself the coward if I left them, my Lord
    Howard,
To these Inquisition dogs and the devildoms of Spain.'

III

So Lord Howard past away with five ships of war that day,
Till he melted like a cloud in the silent summer heaven;
But Sir Richard bore in hand all his sick men from the land
Very carefully and slow,
Men of Bideford in Devon,
And we laid them on the ballast down below;
For we brought them all aboard,
And they blest him in their pain, that they were not left to
    Spain,
To the thumbscrew and the stake, for the glory of the Lord.

IV

He had only a hundred seamen to work the ship and to fight,
And he sailed away from Flores till the Spaniard came in sight,
With his huge sea-castles heaving upon the weather bow.
'Shall we fight or shall we fly?
Good Sir Richard, tell us now,
For to fight is but to die!
There'll be little of us left by the time this sun be set.'
And Sir Richard said again: 'We be all good English men.
Let us bang these dogs of Seville, the children of the devil,
For I never turned my back upon Don or devil yet.'

V

Sir Richard spoke and he laughed, and we roared a hurrah,
    and so
The little Revenge ran on sheer into the heart of the foe,
With her hundred fighters on deck, and her ninety sick below;
For half of their fleet to the right and half to the left were seen,
And the little Revenge ran on through the long sea-lane between.

VI

Thousands of their soldiers looked down from their decks and
    laughed,
Thousands of their seamen made mock at the mad little craft
Running on and on, till delayed
By their mountain-like San Philip that, of fifteen hundred tons,
And up-shadowing high above us with her yawning tiers of guns,
Took the breath from our sails, and we stayed.

VII

And while now the great San Philip hung above us like a cloud
Whence the thunderbolt will fall
Long and loud,
Four galleons drew away
From the Spanish fleet that day,
And two upon the larboard and two upon the starboard lay,
And the battle-thunder broke from them all.

VIII

But anon the great San Philip, she bethought herself and went
Having that within her womb that had left her ill content;
And the rest they came aboard us, and they fought us hand to
    hand,
For a dozen times they came with their pikes and musqueteers,
And a dozen times we shook 'em off as a dog that shakes his
    ears
When he leaps from the water to the land.

IX

And the sun went down, and the stars came out far over the
    summer sea,
But never a moment ceased the fight of the one and the fifty-
    three.
Ship after ship, the whole night long, their high-built galleons
    came,
Ship after ship, the whole night long, with her battle-thunder
    and flame;
Ship after ship, the whole night long, drew back with her dead
    and her shame.
For some were sunk and many were shattered, and so could
    fight us no more –
God of battles, was ever a battle like this in the world before?

X

For he said 'Fight on! fight on!'
Though his vessel was all but a wreck;
And it chanced that, when half of the short summer night was
    gone,
With a grisly wound to be drest he had left the deck,
But a bullet struck him that was dressing it suddenly dead,
And himself he was wounded again in the side and the head,
And he said 'Fight on! fight on!'

XI

And the night went down, and the sun smiled out far over the
    summer sea,
And the Spanish fleet with broken sides lay round us all in a
    ring;
But they dared not touch us again, for they feared that we still
    could sting,
So they watched what the end would be.
And we had not fought them in vain,
But in perilous plight were we,
Seeing forty of our poor hundred were slain,
And half of the rest of us maimed for life
In the crash of the cannonades and the desperate strife;
And the sick men down in the hold were most of them stark
    and cold,
And the pikes were all broken or bent, and the powder was all
    of it spent;
And the masts and the rigging were lying over the side;
But Sir Richard cried in his English pride,
'We have fought such a fight for a day and a night
As may never be fought again!
We have won great glory, my men!
And a day less or more
At sea or ashore,
We die – does it matter when?
Sink me the ship, Master Gunner – sink her, split her in twain!
Fall into the hands of God, not into the hands of Spain!'

And the gunner said 'Ay, ay,' but the seamen made reply:
'We have children, we have wives,
And the Lord spared our lives.
We will make the Spaniard promise, if we yield, to let us go;
We shall live to fight again and to strike another blow.'
And the lion there lay dying, and they yielded to the foe.

And the stately Spanish men to their flagship bore him then,
Where they laid him by the mast, old Sir Richard caught at last,
And they praised him to his face with their courtly foreign
    grace;
But he rose upon their decks, and he cried:
'I have fought for Queen and Faith like a valiant man and true;
I have only done my duty as a man is bound to do:
With a joyful spirit I Sir Richard Grenville die!'
And he fell upon their decks, and he died.

XIV

And they stared at the dead that had been so valiant and true,
And had holden the power and glory of Spain so cheap
That he dared her with one little ship and his English few;
Was he devil or man? He was devil for aught they knew,
But they sank his body with honour down into the deep,
And they manned the Revenge with a swarthier alien crew,
And away she sailed with her loss and longed for her own;
When a wind from the lands they had ruined awoke from sleep,
And the water began to heave and the weather to moan,
And or ever that evening ended a great gale blew,
And a wave like the wave that is raised by an earthquake grew,
Till it smote on their hulls and their sails and their masts and
    their flags,
And the whole sea plunged and fell on the shot‹shattered navy
    of Spain,
And the little Revenge herself went down by the island crags
To be lost evermore in the main.

A SAINT BURNED ALIVE

No portion of my mind misgives.
Come, strip me: lay me on these bars!
Too slow – too slow: my spirits yearn
To float among the clear cold stars.
I know that my Redeemer lives.
I cannot argue, I can burn.
O Lord! I am not mine, but thine.
Christ is my life, my blood, my breath.
When he comes down to meet his Bride,
Hereafter I shall stand and shine
Clothed in white raiment at his side.
His arm hath plucked me forth from Hell,
He hath moved from me all my guilt.
This is his love ineffable,
He hath baptized me unto death
With fire. I am not mine but thine –
My Lord, do with me as thou wilt.

(*St Lawrence*)

SIR GALAHAD

My good blade carves the casques of men,
    My tough lance thrusteth sure,
My strength is as the strength of ten,
    Because my heart is pure.
The shattering trumpets shrilleth high,
    The hard brands shiver on the steel,
The splintered spear-shafts crack and fly
    The horse and rider reel:
They reel, they roll in clanging lists,
    And when the tide of combat stands,
Perfume and flowers fall in showers,
    That lightly rain from ladies' hands.

How sweet are looks that ladies bend
    On whom their favours fall!
For them I battle till the end,
    To save from shame and thrall:
But all my heart is drawn above,
    My knees are bowed in crypt and shrine:
I never felt the kiss of love,
    Nor maiden's hand in mine.
More bounteous aspects on me beam,
    Me mightier transports move and thrill;
So keep I fair through faith and prayer
    A virgin heart in work and will.

When down the stormy crescent goes,
    A light before me swims,
Between dark stems the forest glows,
    I hear a noise of hymns:
Then by some secret shrine I ride;
    I hear a voice but none are there;
The stalls are void, the doors are wide,
    The tapers burning fair.
Fair gleams the snowy altar-cloth,
    The silver vessels sparkle clean,
The shrill bell rings, the censer swings,
    And solemn chaunts resound between.

Sometimes on lonely mountain-meres
    I find a magic bark;
I leap on board: no helmsman steers:
    I float till all is dark.
A gentle sound, an awful light!
    Three angels bear the holy Grail:
With folded feet, in stoles of white,
    On sleeping wings they sail.
Ah, blessèd vision! blood of God!
    My spirit beats her mortal bars,
As down dark tides the glory slides,
    And star-like mingles with the stars.

When on my goodly charger borne
  Through dreaming towns I go,
The cock crows ere the Christmas morn,
  The streets are dumb with snow.
The tempest crackles on the leads,
  And, ringing, springs from brand and mail;
But o'er the dark a glory spreads,
  And gilds the driving hail.
I leave the plain, I climb the height;
  No branchy thicket shelter yields;
But blessèd forms in whistling storms
  Fly o'er waste fens and windy fields.

A maiden knight – to me is given
  Such hope, I know not fear;
I yearn to breathe the airs of heaven
  That often meet me here.
I muse on joy that will not cease,
  Pure spaces clothed in living beams,
Pure lilies of eternal peace,
  Whose odours haunt my dreams;
And, stricken by an angel's hand,
  This mortal armour that I wear,
This weight and size, this heart and eyes,
  Are touched, are turned to finest air.

The clouds are broken in the sky,
  And through the mountain⁄walls
A rolling organ⁄harmony
  Swells up, and shakes and falls.
Then move the trees, the copses nod,
  Wings flutter, voices hover clear:
'O just and faithful knight of God!
  Ride on! the prize is near.'
So pass I hostel, hall, and grange;
  By bridge and ford, by park and pale,
All⁄armed I ride, whate'er betide,
  Until I find the holy Grail.

INVOCATION TO A DEAD FRIEND

BE near me when my light is low,
    When the blood creeps, and the nerves prick
    And tingle; and the heart is sick,
And all the wheels of Being slow.

Be near me when the sensuous frame
    Is racked with pangs that conquer trust;
    And Time, a maniac scattering dust,
And Life, a Fury slinging flame.

Be near me when my faith is dry,
    And men the flies of latter spring,
    That lay their eggs, and sting and sing
And weave their petty cells and die.

Be near me when I fade away,
    To point the term of human strife,
    And on the low dark verge of life
The twilight of eternal day.

                              (FROM: *In Memoriam*)

'THE SPLENDOUR FALLS'

THE splendour falls on castle walls
　　And snowy summits old in story:
The long light shakes across the lakes,
　　And the wild cataract leaps in glory.
Blow, bugle, blow, set the wild echoes flying,
Blow, bugle; answer, echoes, dying, dying, dying.

　　O hark, O hear! how thin and clear,
　　And thinner, clearer, farther going!
　　O sweet and far from cliff and scar
　　The horns of Elfland faintly blowing!
Blow, let us hear the purple glens replying:
Blow, bugle; answer, echoes, dying, dying, dying.

　　O love, they die in yon rich sky,
　　They faint on hill or field or river:
　　Our echoes roll from soul to soul,
　　And grow for ever and for ever,
Blow, bugle, blow, set the wild echoes flying,
And answer, echoes, answer, dying, dying, dying.
                              (FROM: *The Princess*)

'OVER THE DARK WORLD FLIES
THE WIND'

OVER the dark world flies the wind
   And clatters in the sapless trees,
From cloud to cloud through darkness blind
   Quick stars scud o'er the sounding seas:
I look: the showery skirts unbind:
   Mars by the lonely Pleiades
Burns overhead: with brows declined
   I muse: I wander from my peace,
And still divide the rapid mind
   This way and that in search of ease.

MEDITATION ON A STORMY NIGHT

TONIGHT the winds begin to rise
    And roar from yonder dropping day:
    The last red leaf is whirled away,
The rooks are blown about the skies;

The forest cracked, the waters curled,
    The cattle huddled on the lea;
    And wildly dashed on tower and tree
The sunbeam strikes along the world:

And but for fancies, which aver
    That all thy motions gently pass
    Athwart a plane of molten glass,
I scarce could brook the strain and stir

That makes the barren branches loud;
    And but for fear it is not so,
    The wild unrest that lives in woe
Would dote and pore on yonder cloud

That rises upward always higher,
    And onward drags a labouring breast,
    And topples round the dreary west,
A looming bastion fringed with fire.

(FROM: In Memoriam)

THE FLOWER

ONCE in a golden hour
  I cast to earth a seed.
Up there came a flower,
  The people said, a weed.

To and fro they went
  Through my garden-bower,
And muttering discontent
  Cursed me and my flower.

Then it grew so tall
  It wore a crown of light,
But thieves from o'er the wall
  Stole the seed by night.

Sowed it far and wide
  By every town and tower,
Till all the people cried,
  'Splendid is the flower.'

Read my little fable:
    He that runs may read.
Most can raise the flowers now,
    For all have got the seed.

And some are pretty enough,
    And some are poor indeed;
And now again the people
    Call it but a weed.

END OF A GREAT HOUSE

THEN the great Hall was wholly broken down,
And the broad woodland parcelled into farms;
And where the two contrived their daughter's good,
Lies the hawk's cast, the mole has made his run,
The hedgehog underneath the plantain bores,
The rabbit fondles his own harmless face,
The slow-worm creeps, and the thin weasel there
Follows the mouse, and all is open field.

(FROM: *Aylmer's Field*)

'OUR ENEMIES HAVE FALLEN'

Our enemies have fallen, have fallen: the seed,
The little seed they laughed at in the dark,
Has risen and cleft the soil, and grown a bulk
Of spanless girth, that lays on every side
A thousand arms and rushes to the Sun.

Our enemies have fallen, have fallen: they came;
The leaves were wet with women's tears: they heard
A noise of songs they would not understand:
They marked it with the red cross to the fall,
And would have strown it, and are fallen themselves.

Our enemies have fallen, have fallen: they came,
The woodmen with their axes: lo the tree!
But we will make it faggots for the hearth,
And shape it plank and beam for roof and floor,
And boats and bridges for the use of men.

Our enemies have fallen, have fallen: they struck;
With their own blows they hurt themselves, nor knew
There dwelt an iron nature in the grain:
The glittering axe was broken in their arms,
Their arms were shattered to the shoulder blade.

Our enemies have fallen, but this shall grow
A night of Summer from the heat, a breadth
Of Autumn, dropping fruits of power: and rolled
With music in the growing breeze of Time,
The tops shall strike from star to star, the fangs
Shall move the stony bases of the world.

(FROM: *The Princess*)

A SHIPWRECKED SAILOR
IN THE TROPICS

THE mountain wooded to the peak, the lawns
And winding glades high up like ways to Heaven,
The slender coco's drooping crown of plumes,
The lightning flash of insect and of bird,
The lustre of the long convolvuluses
That coiled around the stately stems, and ran
Even to the limit of the land, the glows
And glories of the broad belt of the world,
All these he saw; but what he fain had seen
He could not see, the kindly human face,
Nor ever hear a kindly voice, but heard
The myriad shriek of wheeling ocean-fowl,
The league-long roller thundering on the reef,
The moving whisper of huge trees that branched
And blossomed in the zenith, or the sweep
Of some precipitous rivulet to the wave,
As down the shore he ranged, or all day long
Sat often in the seaward-gazing gorge,
A shipwrecked sailor, waiting for a sail:
No sail from day to day, but every day
The sunrise broken into scarlet shafts
Among the palms and ferns and precipices;
The blaze upon the waters to the east;
The blaze upon his island overhead;
The blaze upon the waters to the west;
Then the great stars that globed themselves in Heaven,
The hollower-bellowing ocean, and again
The scarlet shafts of sunrise – but no sail.

There often as he watched or seemed to watch,
So still, the golden lizard on him paused,
A phantom made of many phantoms moved
Before him haunting him, or he himself
Moved haunting people, things and places, known
Far in a darker isle beyond the line;

The babes, their babble, Annie, the small house,
The climbing street, the mill, the leafy lanes,
The peacock-yewtree and the lonely Hall,
The horse he drove, the boat he sold, the chill
November dawns and dewy-glooming downs,
The gentle shower, the smell of dying leaves,
And the low moan of leaden-coloured seas.

(FROM: *Enoch Arden*)

THE BIRTH OF A NEW KING

'AND on the night
When Uther in Tintagil past away
Moaning and wailing for an heir, the two
Left the still King, and passing forth to breathe,
Then from the castle gateway by the chasm
Descending through the dismal night – a night
In which the bounds of heaven and earth were lost –
Beheld, so high upon the dreary deeps
It seemed in heaven, a ship, the shape thereof
A dragon winged, and all from stem to stern
Bright with a shining people on the decks,
And gone as soon as seen. And then the two
Dropt to the cove, and watched the great sea fall,
Wave after wave, each mightier than the last,
Till last, a ninth one, gathering half the deep
And full of voices, slowly rose and plunged
Roaring, and all the wave was in a flame:
And down the wave and in the flame was borne
A naked babe, and rode to Merlin's feet,
Who stoopt and caught the babe, and cried "The King!
Here is an heir for Uther!" And the fringe
Of that great breaker, sweeping up the strand,
Lashed at the wizard as he spake the word,
And all at once all round him rose in fire,
So that the child and he were clothed in fire.'

(FROM: *The Coming of Arthur*)

78

A PREMONITION OF THE KING'S DEATH

THEN, ere that last weird battle in the west,
There came on Arthur sleeping, Gawain killed
In Lancelot's war, the ghost of Gawain blown
Along a wandering wind, and past his ear
Went shrilling, 'Hollow, hollow all delight!
Hail, King! tomorrow thou shalt pass away.
Farewell! there is an isle of rest for thee.
And I am blown along a wandering wind,
And hollow, hollow, hollow all delight.'
And fainter onward, like wild birds that change
Their season in the night and wail their way
From cloud to cloud, down the long wind the dream
Shrilled; but in going mingled with dim cries
Far in the moonlit haze among the hills,
As of some lonely city sacked by night,
When all is lost, and wife and child with wail
Pass to new lords; and Arthur woke and called,
'Who spake? A dream. O light upon the wind,
Thine, Gawain, was the voice – are these dim cries
Thine? or doth all that haunts the waste and wild
Mourn, knowing it will go along with me?'

(FROM: *The Passing of Arthur*)

A VOYAGE

AND we came to the Silent Isle that we never had touched at
    before,
Where a silent ocean always broke on a silent shore,
And the brooks glittered on in the light without sound, and the
    long waterfalls
Poured in a thunderless plunge to the base of the mountain
    walls,
And the poplar and cypress unshaken by storm flourished up
    beyond sight,
And the pine shot aloft from the crag to an unbelievable
    height,
And high in the heaven above it there flickered a songless lark,
And the cock couldn't crow, and the bull couldn't low, and the
    dog couldn't bark.
And round it we went, and through it, but never a murmur, a
    breath –
It was all of it fair as life, it was all of it quiet as death,
And we hated the beautiful Isle, for whenever we strove to speak
Our voices were thinner and fainter than any flittermouse shriek;
And the men that were mighty of tongue and could raise such
    a battle cry
That a hundred who heard it would rush on a thousand lances
    and die –
O they to be dumbed by the charm! – so flustered with anger
    were they
They almost fell on each other; but after we sailed away.

II

And we came to the Isle of Shouting, we landed, a score of wild
    birds
Cried from the topmost summit with human voices and words;
Once in an hour they cried, and whenever their voices pealed
The steer fell down at the plow and the harvest died from the
    field,

And the men dropt dead in the valleys and half of the cattle
    went lame,
And the roof sank in on the hearth, and the dwelling broke into
    flame;
And the shouting of these wild birds ran into the hearts of my
    crew,
Till they shouted along with the shouting and seized one another
    and slew;
But I drew them the one from the other; I saw that we could
    not stay,
And we left the dead to the birds and we sailed with our wounded
    away.

III

And we came to the Isle of Flowers: their breath met us out on
    the seas,
For the Spring and the middle Summer sat each on the lap of
    the breeze;
And the red passion-flower to the cliffs, and the dark-blue
    clematis, clung,
And starred with a myriad blossom the long convolvulus hung;
And the topmost spire of the mountain was lilies in lieu of snow,
And the lilies like glaciers winded down, running out below
Through the fire of the tulip and poppy, the blaze of gorse, and
    the blush
Of millions of roses that sprang without leaf or a thorn from the
    bush;
And the whole isle-side flashing down from the peak without
    ever a tree
Swept like a torrent of gems from the sky to the blue of the sea;
And we rolled upon capes of crocus and vaunted our kith and
    our kin,
And we wallowed in beds of lilies, and chanted the triumph of
    Finn,
Till each like a golden image was pollened from head to feet
And each was as dry as a cricket, with thirst in the middle-day
    heat.

Blossom and blossom, and promise of blossom, but never a
    fruit!
And we hated the Flowering Isle, as we hated the isle that was
    mute,
And we tore up the flowers by the million and flung them in
    bight and bay,
And we left but a naked rock, and in anger we sailed away.

(FROM: The Voyage of Maeldune)

A SEA MONSTER

BELOW the thunders of the upper deep;
Far, far beneath in the abysmal sea,
His ancient, dreamless, uninvaded sleep
The Kraken sleepeth: faintest sunlights flee
About his shadowy sides: above him swell
Huge sponges of millennial growth and height;
And far away into the sickly light,
From many a wondrous grot and secret cell
Unnumbered and enormous polypi
Winnow with giant arms the slumbering green.
There hath he lain for ages and will lie
Battening upon huge seaworms in his sleep,
Until the latter fire shall heat the deep;
Then once by man and angels to be seen,
In roaring he shall rise and on the surface die.

(The Kraken)

A DREAM

But round the North, a light,
A belt, it seemed, of luminous vapour, lay,
And ever in it a low musical note
Swelled up and died; and, as it swelled, a ridge
Of breaker issued from the belt, and still
Grew with the growing note, and when the note
Had reached a thunderous fulness, on those cliffs
Broke, mixt with awful light (the same as that
Living within the belt) whereby she saw
That all those lines of cliffs were cliffs no more,
But huge cathedral fronts of every age,
Grave, florid, stern, as far as eye could see,
One after one: and then the great ridge drew,
Lessening to the lessening music, back,
And past into the belt and swelled again
Slowly to music: ever when it broke
The statues, king or saint, or founder fell;
Then from the gaps and chasms of ruin left
Came men and women in dark clusters round,
Some crying, 'Set them up! they shall not fall!'
And others, 'Let them lie, for they have fallen.'
And still they strove and wrangled: and she grieved
In her strange dream, she knew not why, to find
Their wildest wailings never out of tune
With that sweet note; and ever as their shrieks
Ran highest up the gamut, that great wave
Returning, while none marked it, on the crowd
Broke, mixt with awful light, and showed their eyes
Glaring, and passionate looks, and swept away
The men of flesh and blood, and men of stone,
To the waste deeps together.

(from: *Sea Dreams*)

THE KNIGHT OF THE MORNING STAR

THEN at his call, 'O daughters of the Dawn,
And servants of the Morning Star, approach,
Arm me,' from out the silken curtain folds
Bare footed and bare headed three fair girls
In gilt and rosy raiment came: their feet
In dewy grasses glistened; and the hair
All over glanced with dewdrop or with gem
Like sparkles in the stone Avanturine.
These armed him in blue arms, and gave a shield
Blue also, and thereon the morning star.
And Gareth silent gazed upon the knight,
Who stood a moment, ere his horse was brought,
Glorying; and in the stream beneath him, shone
Immingled with Heaven's azure waveringly,
The gay pavilion and the naked feet,
His arms, the rosy raiment, and the star.

(FROM: *Gareth and Lynette*)

THE DECLINE OF THE KINGDOM

DAGONET, the fool, whom Gawain in his mood
Had made mock-knight of Arthur's Table Round,
At Camelot, high above the yellowing woods,
Danced like a withered leaf before the hall.
And toward him from the hall, with harp in hand,
And from the crown thereof a carcanet
Of ruby swaying to and fro, the prize
Of Tristram in the jousts of yesterday,
Came Tristram, saying, 'Why skip ye so, Sir Fool?'

For Arthur and Sir Lancelot riding once
Far down beneath a winding wall of rock
Heard a child wail. A stump of oak half-dead,
From roots like some black coil of carven snakes,
Clutched at the crag, and started through mid air
Bearing an eagle's nest: and through the tree
Rushed ever a rainy wind, and through the wind
Pierced ever a child's cry: and crag and tree
Scaling, Sir Lancelot from the perilous nest,
This ruby necklace thrice around her neck,
And all unscarred from beak or talon, brought
A maiden babe; which Arthur pitying took,
Then gave it to his Queen to rear: the Queen
But coldly acquiescing, in her white arms
Received, and after loved it tenderly,
And named it Nestling; so forgot herself
A moment, and her cares; till that young life
Being smitten in mid heaven with mortal cold
Past from her; and in time the carcanet
Vext her with plaintive memories of the child:
So she, delivering it to Arthur, said,
'Take thou the jewels of this dead innocence,
And make them, an thou wilt, a tourney-prize.'

To whom the King, 'Peace to thine eagle-borne
Dead nestling, and this honour after death,
Following thy will! but, O my Queen, I muse
Why ye not wear on arm, or neck, or zone
Those diamonds that I rescued from the tarn,
And Lancelot won, methought, for thee to wear.'

    'Would rather you had let them fall,' she cried,
'Plunge and be lost – ill-fated as they were,
A bitterness to me! – ye look amazed,
Not knowing they were lost as soon as given –
Slid from my hands, when I was leaning out
Above the river – that unhappy child
Past in her barge: but rosier luck will go
With these rich jewels, seeing that they came
Not from the skeleton of a brother-slayer,
But the sweet body of a maiden babe.
Perchance – who knows? – the purest of thy knights
May win them for the purest of my maids.'

    She ended, and the cry of a great jousts
With trumpet-blowings ran on all the ways
From Camelot in among the faded fields
To furthest towers; and everywhere the knights
Armed for a day of glory before the King.

    But on the hither side of that loud morn
Into the hall staggered, his visage ribbed
From ear to ear with dogwhip-weals, his nose
Bridge-broken, one eye out, and one hand off,
And one with shattered fingers dangling lame,
A churl, to whom indignantly the King,

    'My churl, for whom Christ died, what evil beast
Hath drawn his claws athwart thy face? or fiend?
Man was it who marred heaven's image in thee thus?

Then, sputtering through the hedge of splintered teeth,
Yet strangers to the tongue, and with blunt stump
Pitch-blackened sawing the air, said the maimed churl,

'He took them and he drave them to his tower —
Some hold he was a table-knight of thine —
A hundred goodly ones — the Red Knight, he —
Lord, I was tending swine, and the Red Knight
Brake in upon me and drave them to his tower;
And when I called upon thy name as one
That doest right by gentle and by churl,
Maimed me and mauled, and would outright have slain,
Save that he sware me to a message, saying,
"Tell thou the King and all his liars, that I
Have founded my Round Table in the North,
And whatsoever his own knights have sworn
My knights have sworn the counter to it — and say
My tower is full of harlots, like his court,
But mine are worthier, seeing they profess
To be none other than themselves — and say
My knights are all adulterers like his own,
But mine are truer, seeing they profess
To be none other; and say his hour is come,
The heathen are upon him, his long lance
Broken, and his Excalibur a straw." '

Then Arthur turned to Kay the seneschal,
'Take thou my churl, and tend him curiously
Like a king's heir, till all his hurts be whole.
The heathen — but that ever-climbing wave,
Hurled back again so often in empty foam,
Hath lain for years at rest — and renegades,
Thieves, bandits, leavings of confusion, whom
The wholesome realm is purged of otherwhere,
Friends, through your manhood and your fëalty, — now
Make their last head like Satan in the North.
My younger knights, new-made, in whom your flower
Waits to be solid fruit of golden deeds,

Move with me toward their quelling, which achieved,
The loneliest ways are safe from shore to shore.
But thou, Sir Lancelot, sitting in my place
Enchaired tomorrow, arbitrate the field;
For wherefore shouldst thou care to mingle with it,
Only to yield my Queen her own again?
Speak, Lancelot, thou art silent: is it well?'

Thereto Sir Lancelot answered, 'It is well:
Yet better if the King abide, and leave
The leading of his younger knights to me.
Else, for the King has willed it, it is well.'

Then Arthur rose and Lancelot followed him,
And while they stood without the doors, the King
Turned to him saying, 'Is it then so well?
Or mine the blame that oft I seem as he
Of whom was written, "A sound is in his ears"?
The foot that loiters, bidden go, – the glance
That only seems half-loyal to command, –
A manner somewhat fallen from reverence –
Or have I dreamed the bearing of our knights
Tells of a manhood ever less and lower?
Or whence the fear lest this my realm, upreared
By noble deeds at one with noble vows,
From flat confusion and brute violences,
Reel back into the beast, and be no more?'

He spoke, and taking all his younger knights,
Down the slope city rode, and sharply turned
North by the gate. In her high bower the Queen,
Working a tapestry, lifted up her head,
Watched her lord pass, and knew not that she sighed.
Then ran across her memory the strange rhyme
Of bygone Merlin, 'Where is he who knows?
From the great deep to the great deep he goes.'

But when the morning of a tournament,
By these in earnest those in mockery called
The Tournament of the Dead Innocence,
Brake with a wet wind blowing, Lancelot,
Round whose sick head all night, like birds of prey,
The words of Arthur flying shrieked, arose,
And down a streetway hung with folds of pure
White samite, and by fountains running wine,
Where children sat in white with cups of gold,
Moved to the lists, and there, with slow sad steps
Ascending, filled his double-dragoned chair.

He glanced and saw the stately galleries,
Dame, damsel, each through worship of their Queen
White-robed in honour of the stainless child,
And some with scattered jewels, like a bank
Of maiden snow mingled with sparks of fire.
He looked but once, and vailed his eyes again.

The sudden trumpet sounded as in a dream
To ears but half-awaked, then one low roll
Of Autumn thunder, and the jousts began:
And ever the wind blew, and yellowing leaf
And gloom and gleam, and shower and shorn plume
Went down it. Sighing weariedly, as one
Who sits and gazes on a faded fire,
When all the goodlier guests are past away,
Sat their great umpire, looking o'er the lists.
He saw the laws that ruled the tournament
Broken, but spake not; once, a knight cast down
Before his throne of arbitration cursed
The dead babe and the follies of the King;
And once the laces of a helmet cracked,
And showed him, like a vermin in its hole,
Modred, a narrow face: anon he heard
The voice that billowed round the barriers roar
An ocean-sounding welcome to one knight,
But newly-entered, taller than the rest,

And armoured all in forest green, whereon
There tript a hundred tiny silver deer,
And wearing but a holly spray for crest,
With ever scattering berries, and on shield
A spear, a harp, a bugle – Tristram – late
From overseas in Brittany returned,
And marriage with a princess of that realm,
Isolt the White – Sir Tristram of the Woods –
Whom Lancelot knew, had held sometime with pain
His own against him, and now yearned to shake
The burthen off his heart in one full shock
With Tristram even to death: his strong hands gript
And dinted the gilt dragons right and left,
Until he groaned for wrath – so many of those,
That ware their ladies' colours on the casque,
Drew from before Sir Tristram to the bounds,
And there with gibes and flickering mockeries
Stood, while he muttered, 'Craven crests! O shame!
What faith have these in whom they sware to love?
The glory of our Round Table is no more.'

So Tristram won, and Lancelot gave, the gems,
Not speaking other word than 'Hast thou won?
Art thou the purest, brother? See, the hand
Wherewith thou takest this, is red!' to whom
Tristram, half plagued by Lancelot's languorous mood,
Made answer. 'Ay, but wherefore toss me this
Like a dry bone cast to some hungry hound?
Let be thy fair Queen's fantasy. Strength of heart
And might of limb, but mainly use and skill,
Are winners in this pastime of our King.
My hand – belike the lance hath dript upon it –
No blood of mine, I trow; but O chief knight,
Right arm of Arthur in the battlefield,
Great brother, thou nor I have made the world;
Be happy in thy fair Queen as I in mine.'

And Tristram round the gallery made his horse
Caracole; then bowed his homage, bluntly saying,
'Fair damsels, each to him who worships each
Sole Queen of Beauty and of love, behold
This day my Queen of Beauty is not here.'
And most of these were mute, some angered, one
Murmuring, 'All courtesy is dead,' and one,
'The glory of our Round Table is no more.'

Then fell thick rain, plume droopt and mantle clung,
And pettish cries awoke, and the wan day
Went glooming down in wet and weariness:
But under her black brows a swarthy one
Laughed shrilly, crying, 'Praise the patient saints,
Our one white day of Innocence hath past,
Though somewhat draggled at the skirt. So be it.
The snowdrop only, flowering through the year,
Would make the world as blank as Winter-tide.
Come – let us gladden their sad eyes, our Queen's
And Lancelot's, at this night's solemnity
With all the kindlier colours of the field.'

So dame and damsel glittered at the feast
Variously gay: for he that tells the tale
Likened them, saying, as when an hour of cold
Falls on the mountain in midsummer snows,
And all the purple slopes of mountain flowers
Pass under white, till the warm hour returns
With veer of wind, and all are flowers again;
So dame and damsel cast the simple white,
And glowing in all colours, the live grass,
Rose-campion, bluebell, kingcup, poppy, glanced
About the revels, and with mirth so loud
Beyond all use, that, half-amazed, the Queen,
And wroth at Tristram and the lawless jousts,
Brake up their sports, then slowly to her bower
Parted, and in her bosom pain was lord.

(FROM: *The Last Tournament*)

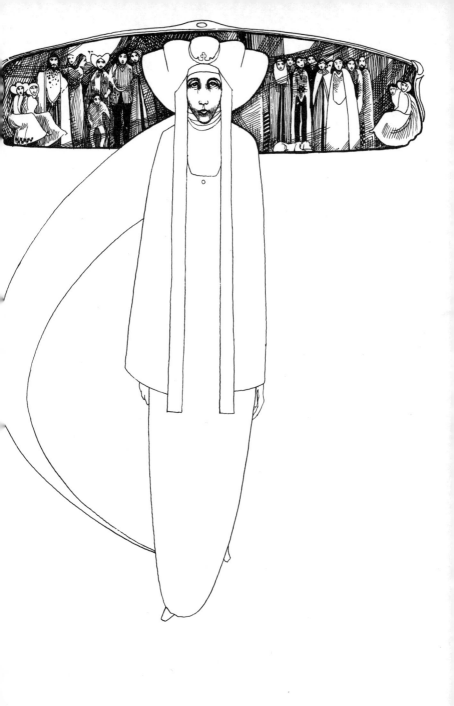

INDEX TO FIRST LINES